Danger Signs

by

Michael Coleman

Illustrated by Nigel Dobbyn

In loving memory of my mother
Grace Doris Coleman (1914 – 2009)

First published in 2010 in Great Britain by
Barrington Stoke Ltd
18 Walker Street, Edinburgh, EH3 7LP

www.barringtonstoke.co.uk

ISBN: 978-1-84299-819-9

Printed in Great Britain by Bell & Bain Ltd

Contents

Chapter 1
"You're Lucky!"

"Are you ready to go swimming?" said Alan.

His brother, Jeff, was looking the other way. He didn't answer.

Alan tapped him hard on the back. Jeff turned round.

"I said, are you ready?" repeated Alan.

"What?" Jeff said.

Alan lost his temper. "Are – you – ready?" he shouted in Jeff's face. "Are – you – ready, Mutton?"

Now it was Jeff's turn to get angry. "Don't call me that!"

Alan just laughed. "Don't call you what? Mutton Jeff? Why not, Mutton Jeff!"

Jeff felt tears come to his eyes. He didn't want to cry, but he couldn't help it. The name his brother called him was so cruel. They lived in London, and in that part of the world "Mutton Jeff" was cockney rhyming slang for "deaf".

"Shut up!" shouted Jeff.

"Why should I?"

"Because you're lucky. You've got ears that work!"

How Your Ears Work

You've got two ears, one on each side. That's really important. If you only had one ear, you'd think every sound was coming from the side that ear was on!

Ears have three parts: the outer ear, the middle ear and the inner ear. It is really only the outer ear that you can see.

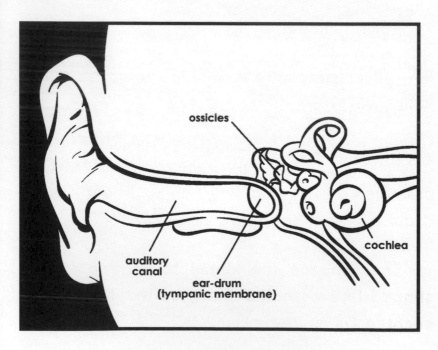

ossicles

cochlea

auditory canal

ear-drum
(tympanic membrane)

Do you think your ears look funny? Don't! Their shape is important! Ears are round because it's the best shape for gathering sounds to send into your ear-hole.

Your ear-hole leads into a short tunnel, called the auditory canal. (Say it: *aw-dit-or-ee canal*).

This tunnel leads to your ear-drum. Its proper name is tympanic membrane (*tim-pan-ick mem-brain*). Sounds bounce against your ear-drum, and make it move.

We've reached your middle ear. On the other side of your ear-drum is a chain made up of three tiny bones, called the ossicles (*oss-sick-ulls*) When your ear-drum moves, they move as well.

These bones are joined to a thing shaped like a snail's shell, called the cochlea (*cock-lee-a*).

The cochlea is in your inner ear. It's a wonderful thing. It turns the movement of the bones into electrical signals.

These signals are sent to the brain – which uses them to "hear" the sound. Amazing!

Jeff ran from the room.

He didn't hear Alan shout, "Go on, cry to Mum. She'll take your side, as always! And if she does, I'm going to the swimming baths on my own!"

Jeff shut himself in the bathroom. He looked at himself in the mirror. His ears looked the same as everybody else's. Why didn't they work?

His mum had tried to explain it to him many times. She'd used pictures of what the inside of his ears looked like. She'd explained how he'd been ill when he was little, and how that had made him go deaf. Jeff knew his Mum had been trying to help, but learning that he'd once been able to hear just as well as everybody else had only made him feel even worse.

That was one of the reasons Jeff enjoyed swimming so much. Under the water, everyone was deaf.

Some Facts and Figures

In the UK, about 850 babies are born badly deaf every year.

About 1 child in every 1000 is deaf at 3 years old or younger.

About 20,000 children aged up to 15 are moderately or profoundly deaf. Of these, about 12,000 will have been born deaf.

When you include adults, it is thought that about 1 in every 7 people (9 million) has some deafness.

Of these, about 700,000 are profoundly deaf.

Alan was getting ready, in the bedroom he and Jeff shared. Alan laid a towel on his bed. He laid his swimming trunks and goggles on top. Then he rolled the towel up and put it in his sports bag.

The local swimming baths were on the other side of town. They still called them "baths" because that was the old name for it. "Baths" was still written up on the stone arch above the entrance to the old and chilly building.

Most days, Alan wasn't that interested in swimming. He thought it was rather boring. He was nothing like as good a swimmer as Jeff. Alan found it hard to do a length, while his brother could do loads of them without getting tired.

Saturday mornings were different, though. Saturday mornings were great.

From 11 o'clock to midday was Fun Hour. Instead of being banned, all sorts of toys were allowed into the pool. The blue water would be filled with beach balls, rubber rings, long blow-up tubes ... you name it.

Best of all, though, taking up most of the pool, would be a huge castle. You could swim across to it, scramble on to it, and then jump off it back into the water.

And the noise! Alan finished zipping up his sports bag. As usual, everybody would be screaming and shouting and laughing as loud as they could. He liked that part almost as much as the swimming.

Blimey, even Mutton Jeff had claimed he could hear the noise faintly – so it had to be loud!

What is Deafness?

A deaf person has trouble hearing sounds that aren't loud enough for them.

Not all sounds are the same! Some people can hear high sounds (like tea cups rattling), but not low sounds (like a bass guitar).

The loudness of a sound is measured in units called decibels (*dess-si-bells*). Here are some examples of the average loudness of everyday noises:

* A quiet room – 40 decibels

* People talking – 60 decibels

* A busy street – 80 decibels

* A road-digger's drill – 100 decibels

* A jet plane – 120 decibels

* A rock concert – 150 decibels

Somebody with normal hearing can hear sounds down to 20 decibels.

How deaf somebody is will be described by the decibel level of the sounds they can hear. There are four main levels:

1. Slightly deaf – trouble hearing sounds under 25-39 decibels

2. Moderately deaf – trouble hearing sounds under 40-69 decibels

3. Severely deaf – trouble hearing sounds under 70-94 decibels

4. Profoundly deaf – trouble hearing sounds under 95 decibels

Chapter 2
What Did You Say?

By the time Jeff came out of the bathroom, Alan had gone downstairs. Not wanting to make his brother any more annoyed than he already was, Jeff got his own swimming gear ready quickly.

Alan was waiting at the front door. "Come on!" he mouthed.

As Jeff reached the bottom of the stairs, their mum hurried out from the kitchen.

Hardly looking at Alan, she went straight to Jeff.

Making sure that he could see her lips moving, she said, "Have you got everything?"

As she spoke, her hands made signs that Jeff was able to understand.

"Don't worry about me so much, Mum!" cried Jeff. He waved his own back-pack for her to see. "I've got everything!"

"Where are your hearing aids?" his mum asked, pointing at her own ears in turn.

Jeff put his hands to his ears. He'd forgotten to put his hearing aids in. Feeling annoyed, he turned and dashed back upstairs.

At the front door, Alan couldn't stop himself. "Come on!" he yelled. "Why don't you put them in the minute you wake up?"

"Don't shout at Jeff like that," his mother snapped.

Why not? thought Alan. *He can't hear me.*

His mum turned to him. "Make sure he doesn't forget to take his hearing aids out when you get to the swimming baths," she said. "If water gets in to them, they'll be ruined."

Alan felt another flash of anger. As she'd spoken, his mum had been making hand signs, as if he too was deaf.

"Help your brother, Alan," she said. Making her right hand into a fist shape, she placed it in the palm of her left hand. It was the sign, Alan knew, for the word "help".

"Yes, yes," said Alan in a sour voice.

Jeff was standing at the top of the stairs and was about to come down again. Alan dug out his iPod, and plugged in its ear-phones. Their mum turned to go back to the kitchen. Even her parting words made Alan annoyed.

"And don't play your music too loud," she said. "I don't want you going deaf as well."

Causes of Deafness

* Your outer ear could be blocked by something. It could be your finger, or a pea! More likely, it will be wax. A blockage stops sounds reaching your ear-drum.

* Some children suffer from what's called "glue ear", an infection which causes their ears to become bunged up.

* Your ear-drum could be damaged. It won't work properly if it's got a tiny hole in it, for example. (This is called a perforated ear-drum.) So don't stick a sharpened pencil in your ear!

* Ear-drums can also be damaged by infections, and even by nasty bangs on the head.

* The little bones (called the ossicles chain) in your middle ear aren't working

properly. This happens a lot with older people. Their ossicles bones get stiff and stop moving smoothly. If this happens, the sounds picked up by your ear-drum don't reach the cochlea.

* The snail's shell cochlea of your inner ear isn't working. Signals aren't being sent to your brain. This means that, even though everything else might be OK, you still can't hear.

The worst type of deafness is when the sound signals don't get from the inner ear to the brain because the connections have been damaged. This damage can be caused by:

* Loud noises – especially if they happen day after day. That's why people who dig roads or work in noisy factories wear ear defenders.

* Viruses. Catching illnesses like mumps or meningitis can also do it.

* Taking too many drugs – even those that are supposed to help you, like antibiotics.

* Getting older.

Young people can suffer this kind of hearing loss too.

* Playing an iPod or personal stereo too loud for too long can be as bad as using a noisy machine every day!

* Babies can be born with damaged hearing if their mum is unlucky enough to catch German measles (rubella) before they're born.

Jeff hated his hearing aids; hated them with a passion.

Even though the ear-piece fitted in his ear – rather like those of Alan's iPod – and the main part was tucked pretty much out of sight behind his ear, he still felt aware of them all the time.

He knew they were there, even if nobody else did. They made him feel different. And they certainly didn't turn his hearing into anything like normal. They helped, sure, but there was still plenty he missed. He couldn't always catch what the presenters on TV were saying, for example. And as for having a mobile phone, like Alan – there was no point. He'd have to hold it above his ear, so that his hearing aid could pick up what was being said. It would make him look like an idiot.

Helping Deaf People Hear

Nowadays the good news is that many hearing problems can be helped by doctors. It might need an operation, but:

* Blocked ears can be unblocked

* Damaged ear-drums can be fixed

* Ossicle bones and even cochleas can be replaced!

An operation might not be the best thing, though. They can be dangerous, and if they don't work can leave the deaf person worse off than before.

That's why the most common type of help is the hearing aid.

* Hearing aids come in different shapes and sizes. Some fit right in the ear canal and can hardly be seen; others have a

part which fits in the ear and is connected by a thin tube to a part that tucks behind the ear.

* Sounds are picked up by the aid and made louder. Really clever aids have a tiny computer which can be programmed to help only the sounds that the deaf person is having trouble with!

* But ... hearing aids can only help a deaf person. They might not help enough at a crowded party, or on a windy day. And they can never make their hearing as good as that of somebody who isn't deaf.

"What did you say?" Jeff asked Alan as they got close to the shopping centre.

Alan repeated what he'd just said. "My mates will think we're not coming. I told them we'd be here by 10:30."

Jeff looked at his watch. They were only a few minutes late.

"They'll wait, won't they? Where did you say we'd meet them?"

"By the entrance."

"Where?" asked Jeff, because his brother's words had been drowned out by the sound of the gusting wind.

"By the entrance!" shouted Alan angrily.

"Which one?" asked Jeff.

Alan looked annoyed, but this time at himself. He just shook his head. He hadn't told his friends which one. And, from the way he'd been patting at his pockets, hadn't remembered his mobile phone so that he could ring and tell them.

The centre had two entrances. They were just arriving at the front entrance. If Alan's friends weren't there then it could mean they were waiting at the back entrance. It would take a good five minutes to walk there.

As they arrived at the front entrance, the automatic doors slid open. Jeff had been hoping that his brother's friends were waiting inside, out of the wind. But there was no sign of them.

"They'll have already left," snapped Alan. He poked a finger at Jeff. "Because of you."

Jeff didn't think it had been his fault, but he tried to make it up to Alan anyway. "Do you want me to go to the back entrance and see if they're waiting there?" he said.

Alan shook his head. "No, I'll go."

"Where will I see you, then?" asked Jeff.

"Wait here for five minutes," said Alan. "Then meet me at The Paths."

The Paths was the name of a burger stall. It was outside the shopping centre, at a kind of crossroads where different pathways met. One of them led on to the swimming baths.

"OK," said Jeff – then he had a sudden thought. Had his brother really said "The Paths"? Or had he said "the Baths"?

Alan was already turning to hurry away. For a moment, Jeff thought of calling him back to ask him to repeat what he'd said.

Then he changed his mind. Sometimes he simply got fed up asking people to repeat themselves. It made them annoyed, and made him feel stupid.

The Paths, Jeff decided. He'd been trying to read Alan's lips as he spoke and the last word he'd said certainly looked like that.

He checked his watch and settled down to wait for five minutes.

Lip Reading

Deaf people are sometimes able to lip-read – that is, work out what a person is saying by watching the way their lips move.

So, if you're talking to a deaf person, face them! Lip-reading isn't easy at the best of times, but lip-readers haven't got a chance if they can only see the back of your head!

Lip-reading takes a lot of effort. Try to speak slower than normal (but – not – a – word – at – a – time – because – that's – very – annoying!)

Keep in mind that a lip-reader will also have trouble if you mumble (or have a beard!)

Lastly, don't expect a lip-reader to get everything right. You may have to repeat what you've said because the lip movements for many words look exactly the same. Stand in front of a mirror and say "path" and "bath" and you'll see that for yourself.

Chapter 3
Where Are They?

But after the five minutes had passed, Jeff was still on his own.

Alan must have met his friends at the back entrance, he thought. They would have gone to The Paths and would be there waiting for him.

Jeff hurried out of the shopping centre's main entrance and turned left. From there he ran a hundred metres or so along the wide pavement. Then he turned left again. A tree-lined pathway stretched out before him, curving its way through a large area of gardens and lawns. This, he knew, would meet up with other pathways in the middle of the gardens. Alan and his friends would have taken one of them as they left the far end of the shopping centre.

Running now, Jeff reached the crossroads they called "The Paths" in less than a minute.

They weren't there.

Had he got it wrong? Jeff wondered. It seemed so. His brother must have said, "Meet me at the Baths" – not "Meet me at The Paths". But if he hadn't …

Jeff sighed. This sort of thing happened so often. He'd not quite follow what was being said, be ashamed to ask for something to be repeated, and it would end up with him getting things wrong. No wonder Alan got so annoyed with him.

Alan was still annoyed.

He'd blamed Jeff for their being late, ignoring the fact that he'd forgotten to tell his friends which entrance they'd meet at. After he'd left Jeff at the main entrance, Alan found them waiting at the back entrance.

"Shall we go and fetch your brother?" one had asked.

Alan had shaken his head. "I told him we'd meet him at the Baths," he'd said. "Come on, let's go. We're late as it is."

Now, after the walk to the Baths, he was waiting impatiently for Jeff to arrive. Others had already bought their tickets and run past them in to the changing rooms.

Alan kicked angrily at the ground. "By the time we get in it'll be packed," he said. He looked at his watch again. More swimmers were hurrying towards them. He made up his mind.

"Come on, let's go in."

"What about Jeff?" asked one of Alan's friends.

"He'll have to find us, won't he?" said Alan. "I'm not his mum."

He turned on his heel and stomped off towards the changing rooms.

As Alan was getting changed, Jeff left The Paths. He was very late now, and it would take him another few minutes to reach the swimming baths. He hoped Alan would go in without waiting for him. He dreaded to think how annoyed his brother would be if he was still waiting when Jeff got there.

And yet ... was it really all his fault? thought Jeff as he ran. Alan could help him more, if he wanted. He could use hand signs, like his mum did. That was really helpful. By lip-reading and watching the hand signs Jeff could work out what was being said to him most of the time.

Even simple finger-spelling would help – that is, using hand signs for different letters of the alphabet. If Alan had made the sign for the letter "B" when he'd said "Baths" then there'd have been no way that Jeff could have mistaken it for "Paths". The signs were completely different.

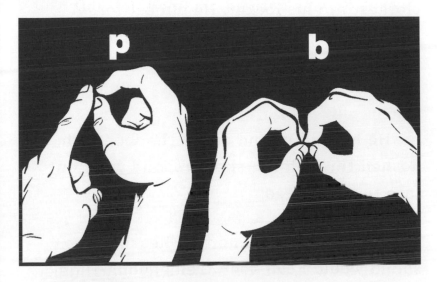

The thing was, Alan knew how to finger-spell. He could remember his mum teaching them both together. He knew plenty of other signs, too. But he just wouldn't use them. "I'm not the deaf one," he'd say under his breath.

Finally, Jeff ran up the steps and through the doors of the Baths. He bought his ticket and dashed into the changing rooms. They were empty.

Fun Hour must have begun. Alan and his friends must be in the pool already. Jeff got changed as quickly as he could. He stuffed his clothes into his locker. He almost forgot about taking out his hearing aids, and had to open his locker again to put them safely inside.

He hopped in and out of the foot bath, dashed through the showers, and went out into the pool area.

To anybody with normal hearing, the sound would have been tremendous. High-pitched laughs and squeals bounced off the walls. For Jeff it was as though he was already under water. The laughs sounded faint, and the squeals were muffled.

But at least he was here.

"Now where are they?" he said to himself.

Chapter 4
Help Me!

Jeff didn't just jump in to the pool.

Instead he walked along the side of the pool, the tiles slick with water.

He passed the pair of lifeguards who were supposed to be watching what was going on. They weren't. They were talking to two pretty girls.

The pool was packed. In the shallow end, younger children were splashing around with beach balls and rubber rings. Some were paddling up and down on body boards.

But most of those there were out in the middle of the pool. There, the big inflatable castle was rocking backwards and forwards, up and down, as people scrambled on to it then jumped off again.

Jeff didn't simply jump in and swim across to it. He wanted to see where his brother was first.

He gazed out at the collection of bodies. Then he saw him. Standing on the far corner of the castle, Alan was waiting to leap into the water ...

Alan jumped. Under the water he went, down and down.

As he felt the hard bottom of the pool against his feet, he pushed up again.

That was when it happened. Instead of coming straight up, he found his head bumping against the bottom of the castle.

Alan pushed to one side. This time his head did come out of the water. But, as he grabbed at the side of the castle's base, he found to his horror that he couldn't climb up onto it. One of his legs seemed to be stuck.

He took a deep breath and ducked his head quickly back under the water. Somehow his foot had become trapped in one of the

thick webbing straps that kept the castle
fastened to the bottom of the pool.

Alan pushed his head clear of the water
again. Gripping the side of the castle as best
he could, he kicked his leg backwards and
forwards. It didn't do any good.

He began to panic.

"Help!" he shouted.

Nobody heard him, so loud was the noise in the pool. He shouted again, this time towards the two lifeguards. "Help!"

The guards didn't even look his way. They just carried on talking to the girls beside them.

Now Alan really began to panic. The inflatable castle was heaving up and down, making the webbing strap move around – and him with it. Whenever it dipped, he was being forced under. It dipped now, and down Alan went. He came up again, gasping for air. Still his leg was trapped. If he didn't get free soon, he was going to drown.

Then he saw his brother.

Jeff was standing at the pool. He was looking straight at him. Alan got ready to shout "Help!" again. Jeff wouldn't hear him, of course, but he would be able to lip read it.

But at that moment the castle gave another violent lurch. Alan was dragged down into the water. He felt his head going under. With one desperate effort he did the only thing he could think of. Stretching both hands upwards, he made a sign and prayed that his brother would understand.

From his place at the side of the pool, Jeff saw his brother's head disappear under the water.

After watching Alan jump in before, he'd lost sight of him for a while in the throng of splashing bodies. Jeff had only spotted him again a few moments ago, and his brother had appeared to be struggling. What he saw now left him in no doubt.

Alan had thrust his arms up out of the water. His right fist was in the palm of his left hand. The same sign, though Jeff didn't

know it, that their mum had made earlier when she'd told Alan, "Help him".

Right fist, in the palm of the left hand. Alan was making the sign for "help".

Jeff didn't stop to think. He jumped into the water. Getting through the mass of bodies between the side and the inflatable castle would take too long. Taking a deep breath he pushed right down and began swimming across the bottom of the pool.

It was totally silent – just like his everyday world, whenever he took his hearing aids off.

Above him he could see floating legs. And ahead, becoming clearer with every stroke he took, was the webbing strap under the inflatable castle.

Reaching it, Jeff thrust powerfully upwards to where Alan's leg was trapped.

With fumbling fingers he tugged at the strap. His lungs were bursting. He tugged again – and his brother's foot came free!

Jeff put his brother's arm around his own neck and pushed upwards again. Both of their heads came out of the water. Jeff thrust out one hand and got a grip on a part of the inflatable castle.

Only then did he dare look at his brother. Alan looked pale. His mouth was clamped shut, as if he'd been trying to stop water getting in.

Then he coughed. He began to splutter. His eyes came open. And he smiled.

Sign Language

Many deaf people "speak" to each other by using signs.

Most of the signs are made with the hands – but often arms, face, lips and even eyebrows have a part to play!

Sign Supported English is a version of English, with signs added.

Makaton is a signing system developed especially for use with deaf children.

In the UK, the most widely used signing system is **British Sign Language**, or **BSL**. (The signs in Makaton are taken from BSL.) BSL is a proper language, with a grammar all of its own.

Just like any language, sign languages in different countries aren't the same. There are even differences between the signs used by a deaf person in the south of England to those used by one in the north!

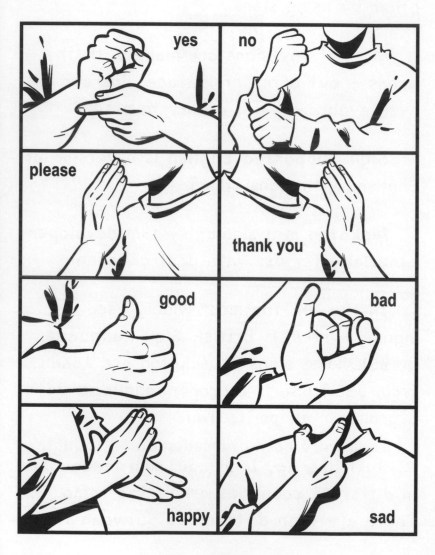

Chapter 5
Thank You

Alan sat in the changing room. He'd begun to feel better and was breathing normally. His face wasn't pale any more. He seemed fine.

Jeff looked down at him. "Are you OK?" he asked.

They were both dressed again, although the Fun Hour was still going on. After the scare he'd had, Alan hadn't wanted to stay in the pool. Jeff had come back to the changing room with him.

Alan hadn't replied. He seemed to be lost in thought.

"Are you OK?" Jeff asked again.

This time Alan looked up.

He clenched his right fist and put it against his chest. He moved it in a circle.

Jeff smiled as he saw his brother make the sign for "sorry". He lip read it too, as Alan said the word as well.

"No problem," said Jeff. "I'm glad I turned up on time!"

But Alan hadn't finished.

Now he cupped his hand and held it against his chin. He moved it away in a looping action. It was the sign for "Thanks".

He held his left hand up for Jeff to see.

Then, with the index finger of his right hand Alan made the finger-spelling shape for the letter "J" – short for "Jeff".

And, as he did so, he said clearly for his brother to lip-read, "Thank you, Jeff."

"Jeff" – not "M" for "Mutton."

Jeff grinned again.

He didn't think for a moment that the two of them would never argue again. But, he hoped, his brother would have more patience with him from now on.

The signs were good, anyway!

AUTHOR FACT FILE
MICHAEL COLEMAN

What gave you the idea to write a book about being deaf?

I'm deaf myself, and so was my mother. Neither of us was deaf when we were young – we lost our hearing as we got older.

Mum had to wear a hearing aid that pressed on the bone behind her ear and was really painful. I was more lucky. My hearing aid is quite light – and I had an operation which brought some of my hearing back. They took out my old ossicles bones inside my ear and gave me new plastic ones. I'm the bionic man!

Have you ever been in danger? What happened?

Not real danger ... but on my first visit to a swimming pool, I felt as though I was. I simply jumped into the water – which was pretty stupid as I didn't know how to swim!

My head went under the water and I started to panic. Then I worked out I was in the shallow end. So I stopped and just stood up! I've never been a good swimmer, though.

Have you any brothers and sisters? Did you get on badly like Jeff and Alan at the beginning of the story, or well like they do at the end?

I have one brother, Barry – and we're a bit like Jeff and Alan. We did a fair bit of fighting when we were younger but we're the best of friends now!

Have you ever saved anyone? What happened?

My family and I were once on holiday by the sea. We got trapped on a sand-bank when the tide came in. There was a safe way back but it would have taken us too long. A storm was coming and the thunder and lighting was getting closer and closer. I put everybody into our little rubber dinghy and pushed them across to safety with the water up to my chin (wishing all the way that I was a good swimmer)!

Barrington Stoke would like to thank all its readers for commenting on the manuscript before publication and in particular:

Lizzie Alder
Gemma Arnold
C. Baxter
Connor Bowyer
Kallem Blewett
Leanne Broadhurst
Curtis Danby
Dominique
Kieran Featherstone
Sam Fergus
Jon Freeman
Liam Gibbons
Joss Gilligan
Amy Hawke
Kylie Hawke
Jacob

Jarvis
Adam Jeffries
Michael Hodgson
Anthony Holland
Leonora
Anthony MacDermott
Jordan Mack
Reece MacLeod
Maisy
Mrs Marshall
Mrs Meeke
Meggie
Sam Porter
Rachael
Katie Rawdon
Jake Reed

James Ribbons
Millie Robinson
Sara
Carla Taylor
Ryan Thomas
Thomas
Sue Tomlinson
Nathan Trafford
Karen Williams

Become a Consultant!

Would you like to be a consultant? Ask your parent, carer or teacher to contact us at the email address below – we'd love to hear from them! They can also find out more by visiting our website.

schools@barringtonstoke.co.uk
www.barringtonstoke.co.uk

Black Death
by
Martyn Beardsley

The year is 1348. When Will comes home from France, the Black Death arrives with him. The terrible illness starts killing people in his village, and those who are left think it's all Will's fault. Can Will and his sister escape the angry villagers ... and the Black Death itself?

Dino-hunter
by
Simon Chapman

Mac Young is on a dinosaur fossil dig in the Gobi desert. He thinks it's boring – all dust and bones – until he's transported back to the time of the dinosaurs! They can smell his blood. They can sense his fear. And they're coming for him. This dino-hunter is being *hunted*.

You can order these books directly from our website at
www.barringtonstoke.co.uk

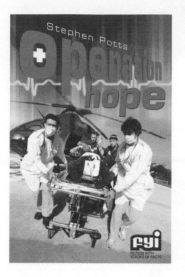

Operation Hope
by
Stephen Potts

David's kidneys don't work, so he feels sick all the time. He can never go on holiday and he's always tired. He's fed up.
A transplant would solve all his problems.
But whose kidney can he get? And will he get through the operation?

Counting on Leroy
by
Steve Mills and Hilary Koll

Leroy loves maths. It's just everything else that's hard! But here's a problem he can't solve ...
1 maths geek + 1 crazy mix-up + 1 star spot on a TV quiz show = 1 big mess! Can Leroy make it all add up?

You can order these books directly from our website at
www.barringtonstoke.co.uk